PETER RABBIT ™

STICKER ACTIVITY BOOK

This book belongs to:

PUFFIN

INTRODUCING...
Peter Rabbit

Meet Peter Rabbit and his family!
Read more about his sisters and cousin,
then add a sticker of each of them.

Peter

A hero in a blue coat and no trousers. He's
a bit naughty and doesn't usually think before
he does something, but he has a good heart.

Flopsy

She loves to dance and has
a lisp when she speaks.

Mopsy

She's great at sewing and makes everyone's coats. She hasn't worked out how to make trousers for Peter yet.

Cotton-tail

Like her brother, Cotton-tail is a bit of a daredevil. She always has her ear to the ground and wants to join Peter on his garden missions.

Benjamin

The voice of reason. He's wise, supportive, a little bit of a worrier and definitely clumsy. He's always there for Peter.

INTO THE GARDEN

Flopsy, Mopsy and Cotton-tail can't wait to explore the garden. Look at the sequences below. Can you work out which bunny is next in line and find the matching sticker?

Who's next?

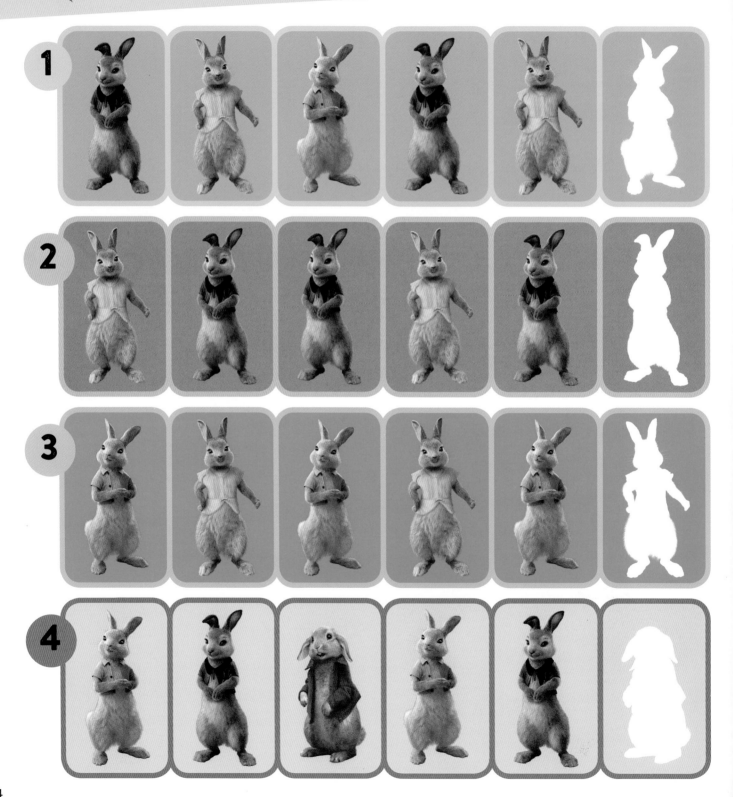

MUNCH BUNCH
Bunny paths

The bunnies have sneaked into the garden. Which tasty snack is each bunny going for?

GARDEN PARTY!

Peter and his friends have taken over Mr. McGregor's garden and are having a party like no other. Use your stickers to add the animal guests below.

Sticker scene

LET'S GO!
Marvellous maze

Mr. McGregor has sent the bunnies and their buddies out of the garden. Help Peter find a way back in for some delicious vegetables.

Pages 2-3

Page 4

Page 9

Pages 14-15

Pages 6-7

Page 13

Pages 14-15

Page 12

SEW CRAFTY

Colouring fun

Mopsy is making a new jacket for Peter. Colour in the coat, then use your stickers to decorate it.

The bunnies have a friend named Bea who looks after them from time to time.
Can you spot seven differences between the pictures of her studio below?

SOMEBUNNY SPECIAL

Cool quiz

Peter and Benjamin are pretty different from each other. Take the quiz below, ticking answers as you go. Place a sticker at the bottom when you know which bunny is most like you!

When you run, you usually:

A. Keep looking forward and run as fast as you can. ◯

B. Keep looking backwards to make sure no one is chasing you. ◯

When you're hungry, you:

A. Take as much as you can. Part of the fun is collecting the food. ◯

B. Take as much as you need. You can always go back. ◯

If a party is coming to an end, you're more likely to say:

A. Not fair! Let's get another party going! ◯

B. It was good while it lasted. I'm glad I have the memories. ◯

You've decided to go to the city. The first thing you do is:

A. Go to the train station, even though you've never taken a train before. ◯

B. Call Johnny Town-Mouse. He's from the city and can show you around. ◯

Your best friend is:

A. A little bit wiser than you. ◯

B. A little bit braver than you. ◯

Answer:

If you ticked mostly "A", you're a bit mischievous but you have a good heart, like Peter Rabbit. If you ticked mostly "B", you're wise beyond your years and brave when it counts, like Benjamin Bunny.

ALL ANIMALS ALLOWED!

Super sudoku

Everyone is welcome in Peter Rabbit's garden. Well, except Mr. McGregor. Use your stickers to complete the sudoku puzzle below. Remember, each animal only appears once in each row or column.

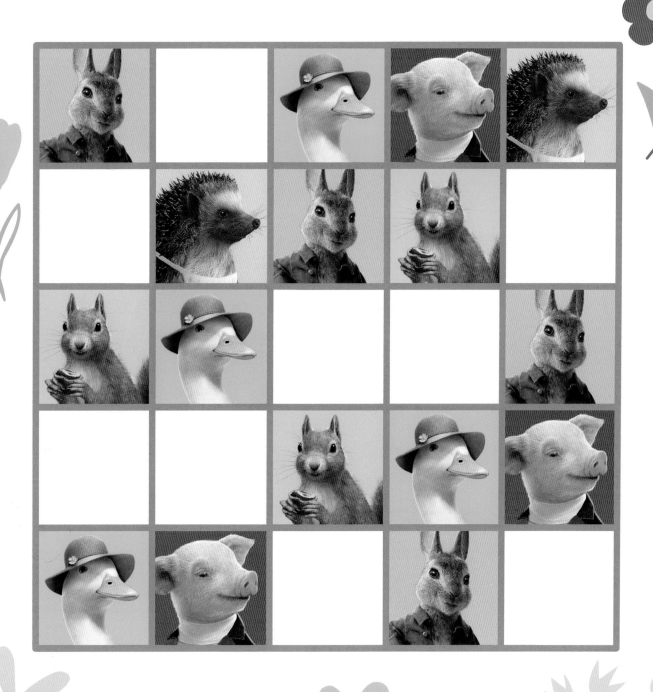

GIVE PEAS A CHANCE

Sticker garden

If you had a garden, what would you grow? Use your stickers on the picture below to create your own green scene!

ANSWERS

Page 4

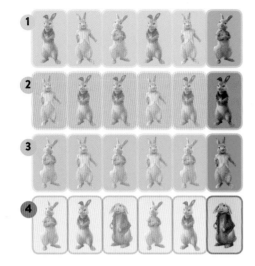

Pages 10–11

Page 5

Page 13

Page 8